P9-EBZ-167

PSP ™

Problem Solving Power

Editor: Christine A. Swanson
Graphics: Karen Clegg-O'Neill

An Essential Learning Product®

Introduction for Parents and Teachers

Solving problems is an important life skill. Essential Learning Products Practice Book 6 contains a variety of realistic life problems to give students Problem Solving Power (PSP).

4 STEPS TO PSP

In Practice Book 6 students are guided through the 4-step plan: READ, PLAN, SOLVE, CHECK. After concentrating on each step, they use the 4-step plan together with the Choose the Operation strategy to attack problems in an organized way.

The numbers have been kept simple. The emphasis is on reading, planning, solving, and checking word problems. Students must have basic arithmetic skills in order to be successful in using Practice Book 5.

PSP STRATEGIES

Students are guided through the following problem solving strategies: Choose the Operation, Draw a Picture, Make a Table, Find a Pattern, Use Logical Reasoning, Work Backwards, Make a Model, Make an Organized List, Solve a Simpler Problem, Guess and Check, Act It Out, and Experiment. Several lessons concentrate on choosing a strategy from a list of four. Students' choices of strategies to solve problems may vary.

TYPES OF PROBLEMS

Students practice solving the following types of problems: Too Much, Too Little Information; Finding Facts from a Picture; Visual Reasoning; and Decision Making. They use their PSP in the last section to practice problem solving. All types, strategies, basic operations, and skills are included.

SELF-CHECKING PROBLEMS

The trivia questions at the top of the page provide motivation for completing the problems. Sometimes the answer is found within the problems. Other times it is upside down at the bottom of the page.

The book is designed for student success in Grade 6. It contains a variety of problems to keep students interested and involved. Using the Essential Learning Products PSP Books gives students the opportunity to build their problem-solving power, increase their self-esteem upon successful completion, and improve their performance on standardized tests.

Contents

The 4-Step Plan

READ

Highlight:
- what is asked
- what is given

Picture the situation.

PLAN

Choose a strategy:
- Draw a picture. ✓
- Make a table or chart. ✓
- Choose the operation.
- Find a pattern.
- Use logical reasoning.
- Work backwards.
- Make a model.
- Make an organized list.
- Solve a simpler problem.
- Guess and check.
- Act it out.
- Experiment.

SOLVE

Use the strategy to find the answer.

Estimate and do the arithmetic.

Highlight the answer.

CHECK

Is your answer close to your estimate?

If not, do the arithmetic again.

Is the answer reasonable?

Does it answer what is asked?

If not, read the problem again and check your plan.

Here's how to use the 4-step plan to solve problems.

READ	Read the problem. $\longrightarrow$ Highlight: what is asked, what is given. Mentally picture the situation: need 80 mg, get $\frac{1}{2}$ of 154 mg.	Your body needs 80 mg of vitamin C a day. An orange contains 154 mg of vitamin C. You eat $\frac{1}{2}$ an orange for breakfast every day. Are you getting the vitamin C you need?
PLAN	Choose a strategy to find how many mg of vitamin C you get in $\frac{1}{2}$ an orange. Write a number sentence.	Use the **Choose the Operation** strategy. Divide the number of mg in one orange by 2. $154 \div 2 = \underline{\quad?\quad}$
SOLVE	Estimate. Do the arithmetic. Label and highlight the answer.	Estimate. $150 \div 2 = 75$ Do the arithmetic. $154 \div 2 = 77$ mg
CHECK	Are the answer and estimate close? Have you answered the question?	Yes, 77 is close to 75. No, $\frac{1}{2}$ an orange does not give you the 80 mg of vitamin C you need.

Using the 4-Step Plan

Use the plan to solve the problems.

READ	Read the problem. ⟶ Highlight: what is asked, what is given. Mentally picture the situation: you need ___?___ $1 bills to pay for 20 29-cent stamps?	You need to go to the post office to buy 20 29-cent stamps. How many $1 bills should you take to pay for the stamps?
PLAN	Choose a strategy to find the amount collected. Write a number sentence.	Use the **Choose the Operation** strategy. Multiply the number of stamps by the cost of each stamp. .29 x 20 = ___?___
SOLVE	Estimate. Do the arithmetic. Label and highlight the answer.	Estimate. $.30 x 20 = $6.00 Do the arithmetic. $.29 x 20 = You will need _____ $1 bills to pay this amount.
CHECK	Are the answer and the estimate close? Have you answered the question?	If not, check your arithmetic. The answer is 6 $1 bills.

READ	Read the problem. ⟶ Highlight what is asked, what is given. Mentally picture the situation: which amount is less, $3.69 – .50 or $3.29?	Mack's Market has Woofy dog food on sale for $3.29. Greg's Grocery offers a coupon for Woofy worth $.50 off its regular price of $3.69. Where will you get the best buy?
PLAN	Choose a strategy to find the price of Woofy at the Grocery. Write a number sentence.	Use the **Choose the Operation** strategy. Subtract. $3.69 – .50 = ___?___
SOLVE	Estimate. Do the arithmetic. Highlight the answer.	Estimate. $3.70 – .50 = _____ Do the arithmetic. $3.69 – .50 = _____
CHECK	Are the answer and the estimate close? Have you answered the question?	If not, check your arithmetic. You get the best buy at Greg's Grocery. You pay $3.19.

Using the 4-Step Plan

Use the plan to solve the problems.

READ	Read the problem. ⟶ Highlight: what is asked, what is given. Mentally picture the situation: 20 days at $1.50 is ___?___ Will the answer be less than $20?	You ride the bus to and from school 20 days per month. Regular fare is $1.50 round trip. A monthly bus pass costs $20. Will buying a bus pass save you money?
PLAN	Choose a strategy to find the total regular fare for 20 days. Write a number sentence.	Use the **Choose the Operation** strategy. Multiply. $1.50 x 20 = ___?___ (total regular fare for 20 days)
SOLVE	Estimate. Do the arithmetic. Label and highlight the answer.	Estimate. $2 x 20 = _____ Do the arithmetic. $1.50 x 20 = _____
CHECK	Are the answer and estimate close? Have you answered the question?	If not, check your arithemtic. The bus pass will save you $10 because regular fare is $30 for 20 days.

READ	Read the problem. ⟶ Highlight: what is asked, what is given. Mentally picture the situation: $26.16 shared equally by 3 friends means each must pay ___?___	You and two friends bought a gift costing $26.16 for a fourth friend. If you want to share the cost equally, how much should each of you contribute toward the cost of the gift?
PLAN	Choose a strategy to find out how much each friend must pay. Write a number sentence.	Use the **Choose the Operation** strategy. Divide to find out each friend's share. $26.16 ÷ 3 = ___?___
SOLVE	Estimate. Do the arithmetic. Label and highlight the answer.	Estimate. $27 ÷ 3 = _____ Do the arithmetic. $26.16 ÷ 3 = _____
CHECK	Are the answer and estimate close? Have you answered the question?	If not, check your arithmetic. The answer is each friend pays $8.72.

The READ Step

Use the 4-step plan to solve the problem.

READ	Read the problem. ⟶ Highlight the important information and mentally picture the situation on your own. Check your understanding of the problem in the PLAN step below.	Maple syrup is made by boiling the sap of the maple tree. If you must boil down 32 liters of sap to get 1 liter of syrup, how much sap do you need to get 6 liters of syrup?
PLAN	Choose a strategy to find the number of liters of sap needed to make 6 liters of syrup. Write a number sentence.	Multiply the number of liters of syrup you want by the number of liters of sap needed. $6 \times 32 = $ ___?___
SOLVE	Estimate. Do the arithmetic. Label and highlight the answer.	Estimate. $6 \times 30 = $ _____ Do the arithmetic. $6 \times 32 = $ _____
CHECK	Are the answer and estimate close? Have you answered the question?	If not, check your arithmetic. The answer is 192 liters.

READ	**1.** Your checking account balance is $358.14. You must pay a bill for textbooks of $79.98. Will you have enough money left to pay for your bike which costs $250?	**2.** In England, people use a weight called a *stone*, equal to 14 pounds. If an Englishman weighs 11.5 stone, what is his weight in pounds?
PLAN	Choose the operation to find out how much money you will have left after paying your bill. Subtract. $358.14 – $79.98 = _____	Choose the operation to convert stones into pounds. Multiply. 11.5 x 14 = _____
SOLVE	Estimate. $360 – 80 = _____ Do the arithmetic. $358.14 – $79.98 = _____	Estimate. 10 x 14 = _____ Do the arithemetic. 11.5 x 14 = _____
CHECK	Check your arithmetic. The answer is yes. You will have $278.16 left in your account.	Check your arithmetic. The answer is 161 pounds.

The PLAN Step

Use the 4-step plan to solve the problems.

READ	Do this step on your own.	It takes you $2\frac{1}{2}$ hours to do your homework. If you want to watch a program on TV at 9:30, what time should you begin your homework?
PLAN	Use the **Choose the Operation** strategy to solve the problem. Should you **add**, **subtract**, **multiply**, or **divide**? Write a number sentence. Check the SOLVE step to see whether you chose the correct operation.	
SOLVE	Estimate. Do the arithmetic. Label and highlight the answer.	Do the arithmetic. 9 hours 30 minutes – 2 hours 30 minutes =
CHECK	Are the answer and estimate close? Have you answered the question?	If not, check your arithmetic and plan. The answer is you should start your homework at 7:00.

What NFL running back gained the most yards in one season?

READ	**1.** Your parents offer you a choice of allowances: $10 per week or 2% of their monthly income which is $1,850. Which should you choose?	**2.** You're a running back on your school's football team. So far in this game you've run for a total of –6 yards. If you want to make +15 yards in the game, how many yards do you have to gain during the rest of the game?
PLAN		
SOLVE	Estimate. $2,000 x .02 = _____ Multiply to find the exact amount. $1,850 x .02 = _____	Estimate. –5 + ? = +15 Add to find the total. –6 + __?__ = +15
CHECK	Check your arithmetic. The answer is $37 a month. Take the $10 per week.	Check your arithmetic. The answer is +21 yards.

Answer: Eric Dickerson; 2,105 yards; 1984; LA Rams

The SOLVE Step

Use the 4-step plan to solve the problems.

READ	Do this step on your own.	Your room measures 12.5 feet by 9.5 feet. Your parents will let you buy a carpet for your room. How many square feet of carpet do you need to cover the floor?
PLAN	Do this step on your own.	
SOLVE	Estimate. Do the arithmetic. Label and highlight the answer. Check the CHECK step to see whether you used the correct plan and solved correctly.	
CHECK	Are the answer and the estimate close? Have you answered the question?	Did you multiply 12.5 x 9.5? Check your plan and arithmetic if you did not get an answer of 118.75 square feet.

READ	**1.** You've built a model rocket. Its first stage measures 15.2 cm high, the second is 27.54 cm high, and the third is 9.75 cm high. You want to display the model on a shelf. One shelf is 48 cm tall, the other is 55 cm high. Which shelf can hold the model rocket?	**2.** Old cassettes are on sale at 2 for $7. How many old cassettes can you buy for $23?
PLAN		
SOLVE		
CHECK	Did you add 15.2, 27.54, and 9.75? Check your plan and arithmetic if you did not get an answer of 52.49 cm high for the rocket. It can go on the shelf that is 55 cm high.	Did you divide $23 by 7? Check your plan and arithmetic if you did not get the answer of 6 cassettes.

The CHECK Step

Use the 4-step plan to solve the problems.

READ	Read the problem. —————————➔	When you buy a bike, you give a down payment of $50 and then pay $15.50 a month for 10 months. What is your total cost for the bike?
PLAN	Do this step on your own.	
SOLVE	Do this step on your own.	
CHECK	Does your answer make sense? Are the answer and estimate close? Have you answered the question?	You would pay a total of $205 for the bike.

READ	**1.** You want to buy a fast printer with your computer. ProPrint prints 37 sheets in 9 minutes. ZipPrint prints 44 sheets in 7 minutes. Which printer is faster?	**2.** Actually, you decide to buy a QuikPrint printer. It starts printing your 30-page report at 6:00 p.m. and finishes the printing at 6:04 p.m. How many sheets does QuikPrint print per minute?
PLAN		
SOLVE		
CHECK	Did you divide the number of sheets by the number of minutes? Did you compare each printer's printing speed? Did you get ZipPrint as the faster printer?	Did you divide 30 pages by 4 minutes? Are your estimate and answer close? The answer is $7\frac{1}{2}$ pages per minute.

Use the 4-step plan to solve the problems.

READ	1. You have exactly $32 in your wallet. You see a pair of shoes you like on sale for $29.99. But you must also pay 8% sales tax on the shoes. Do you have enough money to buy them?	2. You have just won a jackpot. They will pay you either $1,000 for each year you have been alive or $100 for each month you have been alive. Which prize should you choose?
PLAN		
SOLVE		
CHECK	Are the answer and the estimate close? Have you answered the question? Does the answer make sense? If not, check your plan and arithmetic.	

READ	**3.** You use $\frac{1}{4}$ cup of detergent for each load of wash you do. If there are 12 cups of detergent in the bottle, how many loads can you do before you have to buy another bottle of detergent?	**4.** The directions on a bottle of plant food concentrate say that $\frac{1}{4}$ teaspoon of concentrate when added to water makes $\frac{1}{2}$ gallon of plant food. You need $3\frac{1}{2}$ gallons of water to feed your plants. How many teaspoons of concentrate should you use?
PLAN		
SOLVE		
CHECK	Are the answer and the estimate close? Have you answered the question? Does the answer make sense? If not, check your plan and arithmetic.	

Use the 4-step plan to solve the problems.

READ	1. There are about 20 city blocks in 1 mile. If you live $6\frac{1}{2}$ blocks from school and walk to and from school 5 days a week, how many miles do you walk?	2. You buy 150 T-shirts at the wholesale price of $300 for the lot. When you sell the shirts, you want to double what you paid for them. How much should you charge for each T-shirt you sell?
PLAN		
SOLVE		
CHECK	Are the answer and the estimate close? Have you answered the question? Does the answer make sense? If not, check your plan and arithmetic.	

READ	3. The scale used on a road map is 1 inch = 15 miles. You measure the distance on the map from your house to your friend's new town and find it is $8\frac{1}{2}$ inches. How many miles away does your friend live?	4. Your family's car gets 24 miles to the gallon of gas. How much gas would be used, round trip, to visit your friend?
PLAN		
SOLVE		
CHECK	Are the answer and estimate close? Have you answered the question? Does the answer make sense? If not, check your plan and arithmetic.	

Use the 4-step plan to solve the problems.

READ	1. Wayne loves chocolate candy. A box of Chocos weighs $\frac{7}{8}$ pound; a box of Yummies weighs $\frac{5}{7}$ of a pound. Which box should Wayne buy to get the most chocolate?	2. Underwater objects appear 1.25 times larger than they actually are. If you go scuba diving, how large would a fish 46.6 cm long appear to be under the water?
PLAN		
SOLVE		
CHECK	Are the answer and estimate close? Have you answered the question? Does the answer make sense? If not, check your plan and arithmetic.	

What is the longest known lifespan for a domestic cat?

READ	**3.** You have a part-time job that pays $62.50 per week. You see an ad in the paper for a similar job paying $3,640 per year. If you want to earn more money, should you apply for the new job?	**4.** A mountain gorilla may live to be 40 years old. A mouse usually lives about 2 years. A gorilla's lifespan is how many times longer than a mouse's?
PLAN		
SOLVE		
CHECK	Are the answer and estimate close? Have you answered the question? Does the answer make sense? If not, check your plan and arithmetic.	

Use the 4-step plan to solve the problems.

READ	1. Upon arrival in Europe, you must wait to be checked by customs at the airport. There are 2 customs inspectors. Together they check 40 people an hour. There are 50 people on line ahead of you. How long will you wait to go through customs?	2. To budget your money, you keep a record of how much you spend on entertainment each week for a month. At the end of the month you find that you spent $14.60, $23.12, $17.45, and $19.00. What is the average amount you should budget for entertainment?
PLAN		
SOLVE		
CHECK	Are the answer and estimate close? Have you answered the question? Does the answer make sense? If not, check your plan and arithmetic.	

READ	3. Military time is figured on a 24-hour clock. For instance, 1:00 a.m. is 0100 hours, noon is 1200 hours, and so on. If your brother asks you to visit his army base at 1500 hours, what "regular" time should you arrive?	4. The directions for building a doghouse call for a piece of wood 42 inches long. Should you buy a 3-foot or 4-foot board for this piece?
PLAN		
SOLVE		
CHECK	Are the answer and estimate close? Have you answered the question? Does the answer make sense? If not, check your plan and arithmetic.	

Use the 4-step plan to solve the problems.

READ	**1.** You can type 10 pages an hour. It's 4:10 p.m. and your boss hands you 8 pages to type. Can you finish this job before you leave at 5:00 p.m.?	**2.** To paint a doghouse brick red, you must mix bright red and cocoa brown in a ratio of 4:1. If you use 2 quarts of bright red paint, how much cocoa brown paint must you add to it?
PLAN		
SOLVE		
CHECK	Are the answer and estimate close? Have you answered the question? Does the answer make sense? If not, check your plan and arithmetic.	

Color-blind people have trouble seeing which colors?

READ	3. You spend $11.86, $5.29, and $9.85 on clothes. You hand the cashier 2 bills totalling $30. What bills did you give the cashier? What bills do you get as change?	4. You figure that you can save 15% of your $15 weekly allowance to buy a tape recorder. How much money will you save each week?
PLAN		
SOLVE		
CHECK	Are the answer and estimate close? Have you answered the question? Does the answer make sense? If not, check your plan and arithmetic.	

Multi-Step Problems

Sometimes it takes more than one step to solve a problem. Just solve one step at a time.

READ	**1.** A truck can haul 16,250 pounds. It is loaded with 7,228 pounds of bricks and 4,956 pounds of machinery. The trucker needs to ship lumber as well. How much lumber can he carry?	**2.** The Suárez family is vacationing in Europe this summer. Round-trip airfare for Mr. and Mrs. Suárez is $549 each. Each of their 3 children fly half-price. What is the total cost in airfare?
PLAN	Find the number of pounds he's carrying now. 7,228 + 4,956 = _____?_____ Then find how many pounds he can still put in the truck. 16,250 − ____?____ = _____	
SOLVE	Do the addition and subtraction.	

READ	3. It is 7:30 p.m. You want to watch TV at 8:00 p.m., but first you must type a school report 1,423 words long. If you type 55 words per minute, will you be able to finish typing in time to watch TV?	4. What time will you finish typing?
PLAN		
SOLVE		

Too Much, Too Little Information

If there is not enough information, make up a reasonable amount and solve the problem. In the READ step, be sure to highlight only the information you need to solve the problem.

READ	1. There are 14 boys in Mr. Williams's sixth grade class. Two girls moved away. How many students are in the class now?	2. The Bread Box sells day-old bread at reduced prices. The whole wheat bread is $1.29 a loaf, and rye bread is $1.09 a loaf. Damon bought 3 loaves of whole wheat bread. How much did he spend?
PLAN		
SOLVE		

What makes whole wheat bread whole?

READ	**3.** When Paul got the flu, his doctor told him to take 4 tablets of medicine a day until the pills were gone. If the tablets cost $16.29, how many days will they last?	**4.** There are 500 sheets of paper in a ream. A box of paper contains 20 reams. CopyRite bought 45 boxes of paper. How many reams did they get?
PLAN		
SOLVE		

Finding Facts from a Picture

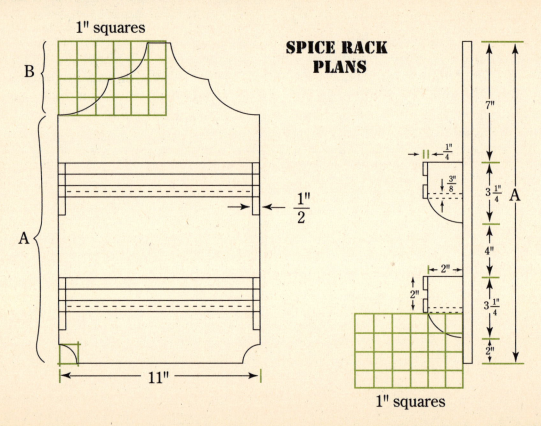

1" squares

SPICE RACK
PLANS

B

A

$\frac{1"}{2}$

11"

7"

$\frac{1"}{4}$

$\frac{3"}{8}$

$3\frac{1"}{4}$ A

4"

2"

2"

$3\frac{1"}{4}$

2"

1" squares

You are making a wooden spice rack as a gift for your grandmother. The directions are shown. Use the information in the picture to answer the questions.

1. How tall is the spice rack (sections A and B)?

_____

2. The decorative top piece is how tall (section B)?

_____

3. You want to buy spice jars to go with the rack. How deep can the jars be?

_____

4. If you want all the spice jars to be the same, what is the maximum height they can be?

_____

5. If the spice jars are $1\frac{1}{2}$ inches wide, how many can fit on each shelf?

_____

6. How tall and how deep are the the curved moldings beneath the shelves?

_____

Problem Solving Strategy: Draw a Picture or Diagram

So far you have used only the **Choose the Operation** strategy in the PLAN step to solve problems. Beginning with this lesson, you will explore other strategies for solving problems.

1. The bottom of a classroom blackboard is 32 inches from the floor. The top edge of the blackboard is 16 inches below the ceiling. If the room is 8 feet high, what is the height of the blackboard?

2. Maria's cousins have arrived for dinner. She must cut the Italian bread into slices 2 cm thick. The bread is 30 cm long. How many cuts must Maria make?

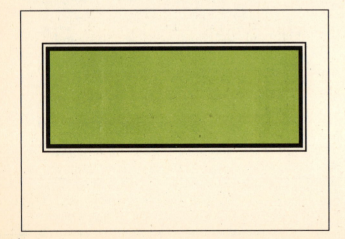

3. You explore your new neighborhood on foot. You leave your house and walk 5 blocks east on Main St., then 7 blocks north on Wall St. You go 1 block west to Church Ave., then stroll 6 blocks south on Church, where you stop at an ice-cream parlor for a cone. How far is the ice-cream parlor from your house?

4. Paula planted a tree beneath her second floor window. Her windowsill is 14 feet from the ground. If the 6-foot tall sapling she planted grows 2 feet per year, how many years will it be before the treetop reaches her windowsill?

Problem Solving Strategy: Make and Use a Table

1. Ella wants to build up her swimming strength until she can swim across a lake 7 km wide. She keeps a record of her daily swims. On Monday, she swims 4 km, and she increases her distance by 500 m each day. On what day will she swim the width of the lake?

	Mon.	Tues.	Wed.
Distance (km)	4	4.5	5.0

2. You are experimenting with growing plants in school. Your records show that on June 1, plant A is 14 cm tall and growing at a rate of 1.5 cm per day; plant B is 6 cm tall and is growing 2.5 cm per day. On what day will plant B be taller than plant A?

3. Answer the questions based on the table shown.

Planet	Distance from the Earth (in miles)
Venus	25,875,000
Mercury	57,312,500
Jupiter	392,937,500
Mars	48,937,500

a. Which planet is the greatest distance from the Earth?

4.

a. Who would have to fly farther to visit Earth, aliens from Mercury or aliens from Mars?

b. If a spaceship flew from Mars to Earth and on to Venus, how far would it travel?

c. All planets revolve around the Sun. The Sun is about 93,000,000 miles from Earth. Which planet listed on the table is farthest from the Sun?

Problem Solving Strategy: Find a Pattern

1. Carlos's class now has computers. There are 36 students in his class. According to the table, how many computers does Carlos's class have?

Students	4	8	12
Computers	1	2	3

2. Donna is planting rows of tulips in her garden. Row 1 has red tulips; row 2 has yellow tulips; and row 3 has purple tulips. If she repeats this pattern, what color tulips will be in row 11?

3. Draw the next figure in the pattern.

4. Arnie was bored. He started writing his name over and over in one long line. He wrote his name 100 times. Which letter did he write in the 96th space in the line?

Problem Solving Strategy: Use Logical Reasoning

1. It is lunchtime at the aquarium for the fur seal, the dolphin, and the orca. The dolphin never eats flounder. The fur seal refuses minnows, and the orca only likes pike. They each eat different fish. Who ate what?

	fur seal	dolphin	orca
flounder			
minnows			
pike			

2. Three horses ran a race. Their names were Sleek, Tweak, and Reginald. Either Sleek or Tweak came in first. Tweak ran second. Which horse came in last?

3. Ms. Wallace's cat had 3 kittens named Sugar, Mitzy, and Boots. The tiger kitten is named Boots. The calico kitten is not named Sugar. What is the name of the black kitten?

4. Vinny, Amy, and Ben each adopted a kitten. Amy picked either Sugar or Boots. Vinny adopted Mitzy. Ben didn't adopt Sugar. Which kitten did Amy adopt?

Choose a Strategy

Choose a strategy to solve the problem.

Draw a Picture	Make a Table	Find a Pattern	Logical Reasoning

1. You're saving your pennies for a $275 CD player. You put 1 penny in a piggy bank the first week, 3 pennies the second week, 9 pennies the third week, 27 pennies the fourth week, and so on. At this rate, how many weeks will it take you to save the money you need?

2. Your camping tent must be anchored with 3 pegs on each of its 4 sides. How many pegs do you need?

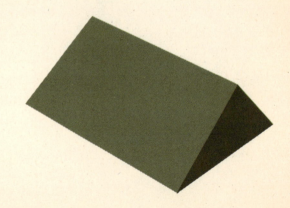

3. Mike wants to improve his accuracy at making free throws in basketball. After practicing, Mike made 80% of his free throws. How many would he have to attempt to make 64?

free throws tried	20	40	60	70	
free throws made	16	32	48	56	64

4. There was a grab bag at the Christmas party. After all the other kids had taken a present, there were 4 gift boxes left: one purple, one green, one red, and one orange. Vic picked the red box. Meg didn't pick the purple box. If Al picked the green box, which gift box did Bill pick?

Problem Solving Strategy: Work Backwards

1. Danielle went to the Sports Emporium to buy a basketball and sneakers. She had $32 in her wallet. The basketball cost $12.95, and the sneakers were $21.95. Can Danielle buy both items?

   She started with $32.00
   She wants to spend $12.95 + $21.95

   Add expenses and deduct from what she has.

2. José dislikes carrying around lots of heavy coins in his pocket. What are the fewest number of coins he can carry if he has the following amounts in change? (He has no half-dollar pieces.)

   76 cents
   99 cents
   42 cents

3. When you add 22 feet to the height of the Eiffel Tower in Paris, France, and then divide by 6, the result equals the height of the Leaning Tower of Pisa in Italy which is 179 feet tall. How tall is the Eiffel Tower?

4. Lori bought 18 cans of soda for her party. If she bought 8 more cans of cola than root beer, how many of each flavor did she buy?

Problem Solving Strategy: Make a Model

1. Darryl's mother bought a frame for an 8-by-10-inch photograph. The top and bottom of the frame are $1\frac{1}{2}$ inches wide, and the sides of the frame are 1 inch wide. What is the size of the framed photo?

2. Manuel works part-time at a shipping company. A worker put 3 boxes on Manuel's shipping scale which showed they weighed 260 pounds. Manuel removed the top box from the scale, and it showed a weight of 185 pounds. When the middle box was removed, the weight was 85 pounds. What was the weight of each box?

3. Stephanie and her mother bought 64 m of fencing to enclose a square vegetable garden. If they attach the fencing to posts placed every 8 m, how many posts will they need?

4. What is the area of their vegetable garden?

Problem Solving Strategy: Make an Organized List

1. Allie's family is planning a trip to England. They want to visit London, Canterbury, and Oxford. They don't know in what order they will visit each place. List all the possible ways they can visit these cities.

2. Josh has 3 crayons: one blue, one green, and one yellow. He wants to color in squares with as many different arrangements of the 3 colors as he can. How many different arrangements can Josh make? Josh will repeat the patterns to fill the grid.

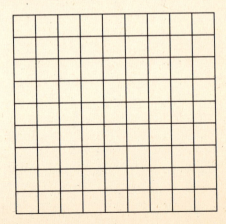

3. How many English words can you make out of the letters S, R, A, and T?

4. How many combinations of letters are there altogether (not necessarily making words)?

Problem Solving Strategy: Solve a Simpler Problem

1. There are 200 people at a picnic in the park. Each picnic table can seat 6 people on each side. How many tables will be needed to seat all 200?

2. At the last minute, 6 more people joined the original group at the picnic. Could they be seated without finding another table? Were there any seats left?

3. A forester counts 18,691 oak trees, 13,277 maple trees, 9,879 hickory trees, and 5,046 fir trees in a large tract of forest. About how many trees are there in this tract of forest?

4. Ms. Triple loves the number 3. Her house has 3 rooms. In each room are 3 closets; inside each closet are 3 envelopes; inside each envelope is $3. She wants to divide this money equally among her 3 grandchildren. Will Ms. Triple have any money left after she does this?

Choose a Strategy

Choose a strategy to solve the problem:

Work Backwards   Make a Model   Make an Organized List   Solve a Simpler Problem

1. How many different squares can you find on a kitchen floor made of 6 rows of 6 square tiles? For example, this diagram can be seen as 4 squares 1 x 1 or 1 square that is 2 x 2.

2. Dan has 3 posters to put up on one wall of his room. One is a poster of his favorite rock band, another is of his favorite actress, and the third is his favorite basketball team. In how many different ways can Dan put up the posters?

3. Greg read 35 books this year! He read 4 times as many science fiction books as other books. How many science fiction books did he read?

4. On Monday morning Quinn noticed that the thermometer outside his window read −5 degrees F. When Quinn got home from school, he saw that the temperature had risen 30 degrees. By Tuesday morning, the temperature had plunged 35 degrees. What was the temperature Tuesday morning?

Problem Solving Strategy: Guess and Check

1. You have to meet your friends at the movies at 3:00 p.m., but first you have chores to do. Cleaning your room will take you half an hour, walking the dog will take 20 minutes, and mowing the lawn will take $1\frac{1}{4}$ hours. It takes 15 minutes to get to the movie theater. What time should you begin your chores?

2. A grocery store has 24 boxes of cereal on a shelf. It has 14 more boxes of Rot-Your-Teeth Sugar O's than it has of Five Grain Good-For-You cereal. How many boxes of Rot-Your-Teeth are on the shelf?

3. You and your friend go shopping. You buy 2 items and give the cashier $25.00. You get $4.00 change. What did you buy?

4. Your friend buys 3 items, pays with a $50 bill, and gets $9.53 change. What did your friend buy?

SALE!

sneakers	$11.50
hiking boots	25.99
jeans	9.50
t-shirts	3.98
socks	2.98

Answer: "Lug" soles, which have a molded pattern giving good traction

Problem Solving Strategy: Act It Out

Work in a group of 4 to act out and solve the problems.

1. Without counting, estimate how many tiles are on the floor or ceiling. Then figure out a simple way to determine the number. Finally, check your results.

2. You are asked to post 12 rectangular pictures on a bulletin board. Each corner of each picture is attached with a tack, but you can overlap the bottom edges of some pictures and the top edges of the next row of pictures and tack their corners together. How many tacks will you need to attach all the pictures if you put them four in a row across?

3. Cut 10 3-inch squares out of red oaktag and 10 3-inch squares out of blue oaktag. Mix all 20 pieces in a shoebox.

a. What do you predict is the fewest number of blind picks you have to make to be certain to get a pair of squares of the same color?

Students take turns being blindfolded and picking squares, one at a time, until 2 of the same color are picked. Keep a record of the number of picks needed to get a pair. Do this 20 times.

b. What was the greatest number of picks needed to make a pair? What was the average? How close to your predictions are your results?

4. Record the exact age of every student in your class to the nearest twelfth. What is the average age of your classmates?

Problem Solving Strategy: Experiment

1. Mindo the Math Whiz challenges you to make 5 triangles using only 9 toothpicks of the same size. Find 9 toothpicks, and create and draw the solution.

2. When Stu flipped a coin 50 times, he found that heads and tails came up about the same number of times. He wondered if he'd get the same results if he spun the coin. Spin a penny at least 30 times. Keep a record of the number of times it falls on heads and the number of times on tails. How do your results compare to Stu's coin tossing?

3. Make a spinner like the one shown. Based on the sections shown in the spinner, make these predictions:

a. Which color will the spinner land on most often?

b. About how often will it land on this color?

c. Which color will the spinner land on least often?

d. About how often will it land on this color?

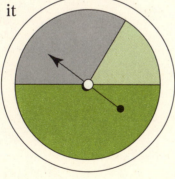

4. Spin the spinner at least 24 times and record your results. How do they compare with your predictions?

a. color spinner landed on most often?

_____

b. percentage of time it landed on this color

_____

c. color spinner landed on least often?

_____

d. percentage of time it landed on this color

_____

Problem Solving Strategy: Visual Reasoning

1. Which of the following figures has the same percent shaded?

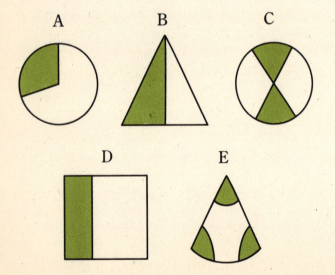

2. Which line divides the figure into 2 identical pieces?

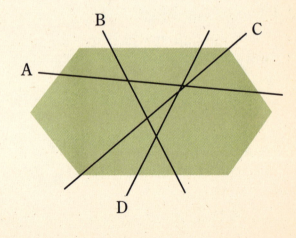

3. You glue 6 small cubes together and then paint the outside. How many cubes are painted on 4 sides?

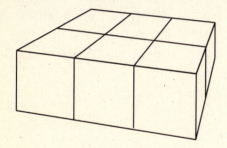

4. Which of these figures can you trace without lifting your pencil from the page and without tracing any line more than once?

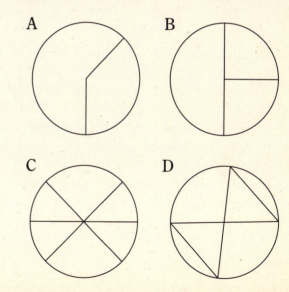

A   B

C   D

Choose a Strategy

Choose a strategy to the solve the problem:

Guess and Check	Act It Out	Experiment	Visual Reasoning

1. Put 1 blue marble, 1 red marble, 1 black marble, and 2 clear marbles in a paper bag.

   a. Predict what the likelihood is of drawing a marble of each color. Experiment by picking 1 marble out of the bag (No peeking!). Put the marble back and draw again. Pick at least 30 times. Record the results for every pick.

   b. How do your results compare to your predictions?

2. The Empire State Building is 102 stories tall, and each story is about 12 feet high. Measure the height of each story in your school building and figure out how many times taller the Empire State Building is than your school.

3. Jerry collects miniature cars. Yesterday he bought 15 cars, some 1950 Chevys and some Model-T's. He bought 7 more Chevys than Model-T's. How many of each did he buy?

4. Which "M"s are symmetrical?

A   B   C

D   E

Problem Solving Strategy: Decision Making

Use the information to solve problems 1–4.

1. You've just helped a neighbor wash his car. The neighbor offers to pay you $\frac{15}{12}$ of $5 or $\frac{9}{8}$ of $5. Which amount would you choose?

2. Tammy is on a diet, but to make her best friend happy she'll eat a small piece of birthday cake. Should she eat the slice that is $\frac{1}{8}$ of the cake or $\frac{3}{16}$ of the cake?

3. A VCR rents for $20 per day. The same VCR sells for $229 new. If you need a VCR for 2 weeks, should you rent or buy?

4. You want to put your money in a savings account. One account pays 9% at the end of 2 years. The other account pays 4.9% a year on your total account balance. Which account should you open?

Use Your PSP

Use your Problem Solving Power to solve the problems in the rest of this book. Use the 4-step plan. Review the steps on page 4 if you need to. The problem solving strategies are listed in the table of contents in case you need to refer to them.

1. During rainstorms, an ocean wave may increase its height by 12 feet. When a very heavy storm hits, this height may double. How tall would a 3.5 foot wave get during a very heavy storm?

2. Suppose you want to divide your odd-shaped garden into 3 equal parts. Draw lines showing how you can do this.

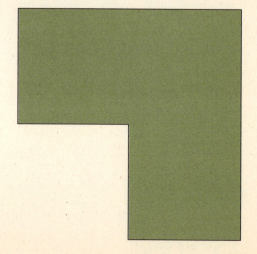

3. The amount of light entering a camera lens is determined by the f-stop setting: in most cameras 1.8, 2.8, 4, 5.6, 8, and 11. The smaller the f-stop number, the more light enters the camera. On a very dark, cloudy day which f-stop would you use to take a picture?

4. a. On a bright, sunny day which f-stop would you use?

b. Which f-stop lets more light into the camera, 2.8 or 5.6?

1. San Francisco is 3,522 km west of Chicago. New York is 1,356 km east of Chicago and 2,978 km east of Denver. How far west of Denver is San Francisco?

2. Chuck took $35 to go shopping for clothes. He bought jeans for $29.75. He saw a shirt he liked, but discovered he'd need another $5.55 to buy it. How much did the shirt cost?

3. Chocolate Chewy is a new candy bar. It costs between 20 cents and 30 cents, and you can pay for it with exactly 6 coins. How much is one Chocolate Chewy bar?

4. You can also buy 2 Chocolate Chewy bars for exactly 6 coins. Which 6 coins would you use?

1. Jamie lives near a small woodlot in New Hampshire. This spring he noticed that of the 180 trees in the woodlot, $\frac{1}{5}$ had died due to acid rain. How many trees were left?

2. Year after year, Jamie noticed that 50% more trees died than the previous year. In how many years will all the trees in the woodlot be dead?

3. Ann is arranging spice jars on a rack. When she places the jars in groups of 5, she has 1 jar left over. When she arranges the jars in groups of 6, she still has 1 jar left over. If Ann has fewer than 40 jars of spices, how many spice jars does she have?

4. Phil is starting a hiking club. Though he is the only member the first week, he plans to ask each new member to find 2 more members to join the following week. At the end of 4 weeks, how many members should be in his club?

1. Each side of a cube is 1 square centimeter. What is the surface area of this stack of cubes?

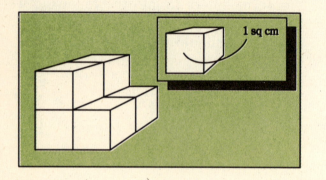

1 sq cm

2. The football team has the ball on the 20-yard line. The quarterback passes and completes to the receiver for 14 yards. On the next play, the running back loses 3 yards. Then a pass is completed for a 9-yard gain. On the fourth play of the drive, the runner gains 4 yards for a first down. On what yard line is the ball now?

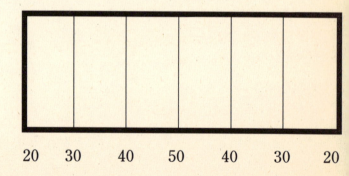

20   30   40   50   40   30   20

When was the first U.S. space shuttle launched?

3. The space shuttle has fuel cells that provide energy for 5,000 flight hours. If the shuttle has made trips of 1,266 hours, 1,011 hours, and 843 hours, how many more flight hours will the fuel cells last?

4. The shuttle's next 2 flights are to be 21 days and 45 days long. Will the shuttle's fuel cells last during these upcoming flights?

1. Emilio batted 30 times in the last month's baseball games. The table shows what happened at each at-bat.

a. What is the most frequent result of Emilio's at-bats?

Result	Number
home run	3
triple	1
double	7
single	11
out	8

2. a. What fraction of the time at bat did Emilio hit a home run?

b. What is the probability of Emilio striking out when he's at bat?

What baseball player had the most home-runs in his career?

3. This year Pedro's mother is 3 times as old as he is. When Pedro was born, his mother was 24 years old. How old is Pedro's mother this year? How old is Pedro this year?

4. Ms. Harris gave her class a history test consisting of 4 true or false questions. How many different ways could the 4 questions be answered?

1. Terry calls Pat a lot. Finally, Terry's mom said she must keep her calls to under $15 a month. Each call costs $.31 for the first minute and $.19 for each additional minute. If Terry speaks to Pat for 15 minutes at a time, how many calls can she make each month without going over her $15 limit?

2. The price of gasoline just went up again. Now, when Mr. Ramírez fills his car's gas tank, he must pay $1.35 per gallon. How much will it cost him to fill up his car's gas tank?

3. A simple code for language involves substituting a number for each letter of the alphabet. For example, a=1, b=2, e=5, and so on. Use this code to figure out the following message:

23,5 8,1,22,5 14,15,20,8,9,14,7 20,15
6,5,1,18 2,21,20 6,5,1,8 9,20,19,5,12,6

4. Make up your own letter/number code and write a message for a classmate to figure out.

1. You decide to sleep 6 hours a day instead of 8 so you'll have more time to do things. If you keep this up for 20 years, how many extra hours (or days) will you be awake and active?

2. Marcia gets her hair cut every 3 months. She discovered that her hair grows 12 inches per year. To keep her hair the same length, how many inches of hair does she have to cut off each time she gets a haircut?

Answer: about 16 hours

3. The map of the trail through the forest to the lake is drawn on a scale of 1 cm = $\frac{1}{4}$ mile. If the map's trail line is $5\frac{1}{2}$ cm long, how long is the walk from the trailhead to the lake?

Trailhead

Lake

4. Ellen has 4 cats, so she goes to the store every 3 days to buy cat food. Roz has 1 cat, so she goes to the store every 8 days for cat food. How often are Ellen and Roz likely to meet in the cat food section of the store?

1. Six houses were built in a circle around a central lawn. All the neighbors are very friendly and, after many visits to each other, have worn pathways across the lawn. There are straight paths that connect every house to every other house. How many paths are there?

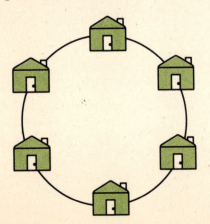

2. You and your older brother play checkers every evening. When you win a game, you get 5 points. When your brother wins a game, he gets 3 points. This week you've played 16 games and the score is tied. How many games have you won?

3. There are 5 horses running a race. Coconuts finished 1 length ahead of Swiftie. Big Boy finished ahead of Coconuts but behind Twinkletoes. Magician finished 4 lengths ahead of Swiftie and 1 length behind Big Boy. In what order did the horses finish?

4. What would you add to balance the scale shown below, and what side would you add it to?

1. Steve went to the county fair and stopped at a booth to play darts. The booth owner said Steve could play until he scored 173 points. Each of Steve's shots hit the dart board. What is the fewest number of shots Steve could throw to make 173 points?

2. What is the greatest number of shots?

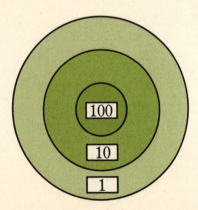

3. Your family asks your advice about which long-distance phone company to sign up with. The rates to California are shown in the table. Which company offers the best weekday rates for a 10-minute call to California?

Dial-Away Co.		
	1ˢᵗ 3 min	Ea. Additional Minute
M–F	$1.55	$.34
S & S	$1.40	$.29

Good Communications Co.		
	1ˢᵗ 3 min	Ea. Additional Minute
M–F	$1.75	$.28
S & S	$1.50	$.23

4. a. You point out that most calls to your brother in Los Angeles are made on weekends. Which company do you advise your family to sign up with?

b. How much would you save with this company for a 10-minute call on Sunday?

1. Amy is putting candles on her friend's birthday cake. Her friend is 16 years old. The dimensions of the cake are shown. If Amy wants to place the candles at equal distances from each other, how far apart should they be?

2. In one city, bike license plates have one letter followed by one single even digit. How many different license plates can there be?

3. The ancient Egyptians had a system for writing numbers. For example, the number 1,233 was written:

Write the following numbers using the Egyptian number system:

a. 47
b. 213

4. a. 1,445
b. 20,311
c. 32,224

Number	Egyptian Number
1	|
10	∩
100	ϑ
1,000	⚱
10,000	↳

1. Mr. Chu, the school principal, loves to joke with students. One student asked him how old he was. Mr. Chu laughed and said, "If you divide my age by 2, the remainder will be 1. Also, if you divide my age by 3, 4, or 5, the remainder is still 1." How old is Mr. Chu?

2. Janine took a long bus ride. The trip took 6 hours. She got bored and fell asleep halfway through the trip. When she woke up, the distance she still had to ride was half the distance the bus covered while she slept. How long did Janine sleep?

Answer: 75 hours

3. a. Use the numbers 1, 2, 3, 4, 5, 6, and 7. Put one number in each box so that the sum of each line is 13. A number may be used only once.

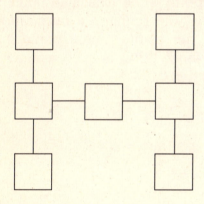

b. How many additional variations can be arranged?

4. You want to buy a bike costing $220. If you pay 50% down, you have to pay 7% interest over the next year only on the balance. If you pay no money down, you must pay 18% interest on the total during the next 12 months.

a. Which is the better deal?
b. How much will you save this way?

1. Your mom baked 3 pies for her bridge party. She says you can take $\frac{1}{2}$ a pie to your friend's house, and she gives you one piece of Pie C. Which pie should you take a slice(s) from so you have exactly $\frac{1}{2}$ a pie?

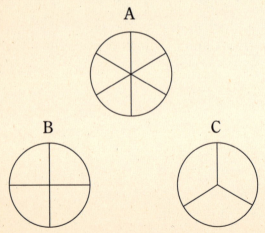

A

B   C

2. Alice, Barb, and Charlene have apartments next door to each other. One is a cartoonist, one is a registered nurse, and one is a dancer. Barb lives in the middle apartment. When Charlene takes a vacation, the registered nurse next door waters her plants. The cartoonist is Alice's best friend. What is each woman's occupation?

3. Luisa helped her father plow $\frac{1}{2}$ a field. Then she put fertilizer on $\frac{4}{5}$ of the plowed area. What fraction of the whole field received fertilizer?

4. Eliot is practicing a technique that will help him dry the supper dishes more quickly. At first, it took him a full minute to dry one dish. He kept a record of his improvement. How long will it take him to dry a dish tomorrow and the next day if his speed continues to improve at the same rate?

	Start	Day 2	Day 3	Day 4	Today	Tomorrow	Day after
# secs	1	$\frac{9}{10}$	$\frac{4}{5}$	$\frac{7}{10}$	$\frac{3}{5}$		

1. Fill in the missing numbers so that each column, row, and diagonal adds up to -6.

	–14	+1
–5	+10	

2. At the county fair, prizes are offered in each of 12 contests: first place is $100; second place is $65; third place is $40. Every contest participant pays $15 to enter. How much prize money is paid out all together? How many contestants must enter the contests to cover the cost of the prize money?

3. Naomi built a model of her dream house. She built it to scale at a ratio of 20:1. Her model house is $4\frac{1}{2}$ feet long, 3 feet wide, and 2 feet high. What are the dimensions of her dream house?

4. Barry, Jason, and Derek are bored on a rainy Saturday afternoon. One wants to play Ping-Pong, another wants to watch TV, and the third would rather play Monopoly. Barry and the boy who wants to play Monopoly drank soda. The boy who wanted to watch TV and the boy who wanted to play Monopoly talked about baseball. Jason does not like TV or soda. Who wanted to do what?

Answers

Page 18, 19
1. No. The cost is $32.39 with tax.
2. $100 per month = $1,200 per year
3. 48 laundries
4. $1\frac{3}{4}$ teaspoons

Page 20, 21
1. 65 blocks = $3\frac{1}{4}$ miles
2. $4 each
3. $127\frac{1}{2}$ miles
4. 10.625 (10.63) gallons

Page 22, 23
1. Chocos, you get $\frac{9}{56}$ more.
2. appears to be 58.25 cm long
3. Yes. The new job pays $70 a week.
4. 20 times longer

Page 24, 25
1. 75 minutes = $1\frac{1}{4}$ hour wait
2. $18.54
3. 3:00 p.m.
4. 4-foot board = 48 inches

Page 26, 27
1. Yes. It will take you 48 minutes, and you leave in 50.
2. $\frac{1}{2}$ quart of cocoa brown paint
3. gave 1 $20 bill and 1 $10 bill; got back 3 $1 bills
4. save $2.25 per week

Page 28, 29
1. 4,066 pounds
2. $1,921.50
3. yes
4. about 7:56 p.m.

Page 30, 31
1. can't tell
2. $3.87
3. can't tell
4. 900 reams

Page 33
1. $19\frac{1}{2}$ inches
2. 4 inches
3. 2 inches
4. 6 inches
5. 7
6. 2 inches deep, 3 inches tall

Page 34, 35
1. 4 feet
2. 14 cuts = 15 slices
3. 5 blocks
4. 4 years

Page 36, 37
1. Sunday
2. June 10
3. a. Jupiter

4. a. Mercury
   b. 74,812,500 miles
   c. Jupiter

Page 38, 39
1. 9 computers
2. yellow tulips
3.

4. the letter A

Page 40, 41
1. The dolphin ate minnows; the fur seal ate flounder; the orca ate pike.
2. Reginald came in last
3. Sugar
4. Sugar

Page 42, 43
1. 10 weeks
2. 8 pegs
3. 80
4. purple

Page 44, 45
1. No, she needs an additional $2.90.
2. $.76 = 4 coins (3q, 1p)
   $.99 = 9 coins (3q, 2d, 4p)
   $.42 = 5 coins (1q, 1d, 1n, 2p)
3. 1,052 feet tall
4. 13 cola, 5 root beer

Page 46, 47
1. 11 x 12 inches
2. box 1 = 75 lbs; box 2 = 100 lbs; box 3 = 85 lbs
3. 8 posts
4. 256 square meters

Page 48, 49
1. LCO, LOC, CLO, COL, OLC, OCL
2. 6 arrangements: bgy, byg, gby, gyb, ybg, ygb
3. 4: arts, star, rats, tars
4. 24

Page 50, 51
1. 9 tables
2. yes; yes, 2
3. about 47,000; exactly 46,893 trees
4. No.

Page 52, 53
1. 91 squares
2. 6 different ways
3. 28
4. −10 degrees F

Page 54, 55
1. 12:40 p.m.
2. 19 boxes
3. sneakers and jeans
4. sneakers, hiking boots, and socks

Page 56, 57
1. Answers will vary, but multiply number of tiles wide by # of tiles long.

2. 32 thumbtacks
3. a. 3 picks
   b. answers will vary
4. Answers will vary.

Page 58, 59
1.

2. Answers will vary, but since the head side of a coin is slightly heavier than the tail side, a spun coin should land more often with tails up.
3. Answers will vary.
4. Answers will vary, but should be close to fraction/percent of the circle each color occupies.

Page 60, 61
1. figures A, C, and D
2. line C
3. 4 cubes
4. figures A and D

Page 62, 63
1. a. should predict clear marbles $\frac{2}{5}$ likelihood; other $\frac{1}{5}$
   b. Answers will vary.
2. Answers will vary.
3. 11 Chevys; 4 Model-T's
4. figures A and C

Page 64, 65
1. $\frac{15}{12}$ $(\frac{5}{4})$
2. $\frac{1}{8}$
3. You should buy. You save $51.
4. 4.9% account

Page 66, 67
1. 31 feet tall
2.

3. f 1.8
4. a. f 11
   b. f 2.8

Page 68, 69
1. 1,900 km
2. $10.80
3. 24 cents– 2d, 4p
4. 48 cents– 1q, 2d, 3p

Page 70, 71
1. 144
2. 4 years

	year 1	year 2	year 3	year 4
	36 die	54 die	81 die	all dead
	144 left	90 left	9 left	

3. 31
4. 15

Page 72, 73
1. 22 square centimeters
2. 44 yard line
3. 1,880 hours
4. Yes, it has up to 78 days fuel.

Page 74, 75
1. a. single
2. b. $\frac{1}{10}$

   c. $\frac{8}{30}$ or $\frac{4}{15}$
3. mother – 36; Pedro – 12
4. 16 ways

Page 76, 77
1. 5 calls at $2.97 each
2. can't tell; too little information
3. We have nothing to fear but fear itself.
4. Answers will vary.

Page 78, 79
1. 14,600 hours or $608\frac{1}{3}$ days
2. 3 inches
3. $1\frac{3}{8}$ miles
4. 24 days

Page 80, 81
1. 15
2. 6 games
3. Twinkletoes, Big Boy, Magician, Coconuts, Swiftie
4. Add 1 cube to the right side.

Page 82, 83
1. 11 shots

2. 173 shots
3. Good Communications
4. a. Good Communications
   b. $.32

Page 84, 85
1. 2 inches apart
2. 104 license plates
3. a. 47   = ∩∩∩∩|||||||
   b. 213   = 99∩|||
4. c. 1,445 = 𐦀9999∩∩∩∩||||
   d. 20,311 = ⌐⌐999∩|
   e. 32,224 = ⌐⌐⌐𐦀𐦀99∩∩||||

Page 86, 87
1. 61 years old
2. 2 hours
3. a. 3   1
      4 2 7
      6   5
   b. 7
4. a. pay 50% down
   b. save $31.90

Page 88, 89
1. 1 slice from pie A
2. Barb, registered nurse; Charlene, cartoonist; Alice, dancer
3. $\frac{2}{5}$
4. $\frac{1}{2}$ minute; $\frac{2}{5}$ minute

Page 90, 91

1.

+7		
−8	−2	+4
		−11

2. $2,460; 164 contestants
3. 90 feet long; 60 feet wide; 40 feet high
4. Barry, TV; Derek, Monopoly; Jason, Ping-Pong